On very dark nights, long before
people knew about smog, men looked
into the night sky. Scribble to find
what they could see.

Every night men studied the stars. They drew pictures of where the stars and moon were in the sky. Sometimes they even gave the stars names.

From watching the sky they learned—

how to make a... 🡕

Some of what men learned by watching the stars and moon on dark nights has helped us . . .

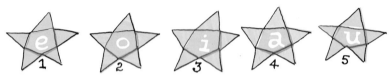

Scribble, then match letters to numbers to read the sentences.

In a country east of Bethlehem, some men who studied the stars, watched the starry sky on the night Jesus was born.

Suddenly one of the men jumped up. He pointed into the sky. "A strange new star!" he exclaimed. "I have not seen it before; have you?"

Scribble the picture and find the strange new star.

The other Wise Men quickly agreed the strange star was new.

"I wonder where it came from?" one Wise Man asked.

"Perhaps it is to tell us something," said a second Wise Man.

"But what?" asked the first.

"The star could be a sign that the Hebrew King has come," said the Wise Man who discovered the star. "The people look for a new leader."

Scribble the picture to find what was happening in Bethlehem.

"Let's go to Jerusalem," suggested the first Wise Man. "And find out if they have a new King."

"They may see the new star too, and know for sure why it shines," added the second Wise Man.

"We do want to learn all we can about the stars; let's begin our journey at once," agreed the third Wise Man.

Help them find the way to the city of Jerusalem.

At Jerusalem the Wise Men asked people they saw, "Where is the new baby King? We saw His star and we want to worship Him."

No one knew about the baby or the star.

"I have an idea," said one of the Wise Men at last.

Scribble to find what his idea was.

King
Herod

Chief
Priests

Lawyers

"A new King indeed!" sputtered ☐ after he saw the Wise Men ☐ called the ☐ and the ☐ to a meeting.

"Where will your Savior be born?" ☐ asked.

"At Bethlehem," the ☐ and the ☐ answered. ☐ sent the ☐ and the ☐ away, and he called the Wise Men to him again.

Scribble the picture to find what King Herod told the Wise Men.

The king asked the Wise Men to return to Jerusalem after they found the baby King. "I would like to worship Him also," the king said.

The Wise Men left the palace and started toward Bethlehem. Scribble the picture to find what they saw.